Carols for Everyone

Seven festive pieces for children
with piano & adult choir (optional)

Published by
Novello Publishing Limited
14-15 Berners Street,
London W1T 3LJ, UK.

Exclusive Distributors:
Music Sales Limited
Distribution Centre, Newmarket Road,
Bury St Edmunds, Suffolk IP33 3YB, UK.

Music Sales Corporation
180 Madison Avenue, 24th Floor,
New York NY 10016, USA.

Music Sales Pty Limited
Units 3-4, 17 Willfox Street, Condell Park
NSW 2200, Australia.

Order No. NOV293810
ISBN 978-1-78305-198-4

Edited by Jonathan Wikeley

Printed in the EU.

www.musicsales.com

Carols for Everyone

Seven festive pieces for children
with piano & adult choir (optional)

Novello Publishing Limited
part of The Music Sales Group
London / New York / Paris / Sydney / Copenhagen / Berlin / Madrid / Hong Kong / Tokyo

The Carnegie UK Trust has supported music making throughout its history. In the 1930s it supported the creation of the National Federation of Music Societies, now operating as Making Music. To mark its centenary in 2013, the Trust has funded this collection to provide high quality material specially designed for the combination of adult and children's voices. It is hoped that this will encourage new partnerships between adult and children's choirs, and strengthen choral singing in communities throughout the UK and Ireland, as well as bringing pleasure to participants and audiences.

The Carnegie UK Trust works to improve the lives of people throughout the UK and Ireland by changing minds through influencing policy, and by changing minds through innovative practice and partnership work. The Carnegie UK Trust was established in 1913 by the Scots-American philanthropist Andrew Carnegie, and has a long history of support for music making, particularly in the voluntary sector.

Making Music is the UK's leading organisation for voluntary music, supporting all kinds of voluntary music groups—bands, choirs, festivals, orchestras and music clubs—because we feel that the more music people make together the happier and healthier we all are. Our 3,000 member organisations come to Making Music for the expert help they need to set up, run and develop music groups in their communities. Whether it is providing members with affordable insurance or advice on everything from audience development to Gift Aid, or simply putting people in touch with their local music group, Making Music is here to help everyone flourish in their music making. We are a powerful voice for voluntary music, working hard to highlight the many benefits of music making.

With over 1,700 vocal groups in membership, Making Music identified a need for music written specifically for both adult and children's voices. We were delighted that the Carnegie UK Trust agreed to support this idea, and we hope *Carols for Everyone* will see many fantastic performances, and allow children and adults to come together to sing.

Adam lay ybounden

(SATB and Children's Choir)

Anon. c. 15th century

Thea Musgrave

Adam lay ybounden

(Children's Choir version)

Anon. c. 15th century

Thea Musgrave

The angel Gabriel

Basque Noël
arr. John Duggan

♩. = 58

CHILDREN

SOPRANO
ALTO

TENOR
BASS

PIANO

mp

con pedale

4

CHILDREN

p unis.

The an - gel Gab - ri - el from hea - ven came,____ His

wings as drift - ed snow, his eyes_____ as flame;_____ "All hail," said he, "thou low - ly maid-en

Ma - - ry,_____ Most high - ly fa - voured la - dy,"

Glo - - - - ri - a!

mp cresc.

* Play cue-sized notes only when performing without SATB chorus.

B

Then gen- tle Ma - ry meek- ly

Mag - ni - fi-cat,   Mag -

bowed her head,_____ "To me be as it plea-seth God,"_____ she said,_____ "My

Oxford, March 2013

To Floella

I Pray

Words & Music: Paul Mealor

This part is only to be sung if no SATB choir is available.
Otherwise, Trebles are tacet until b.25

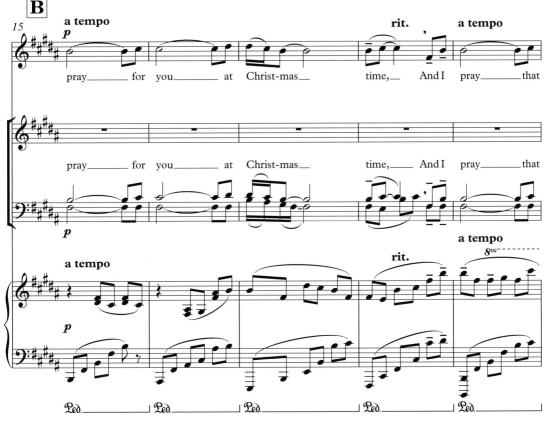

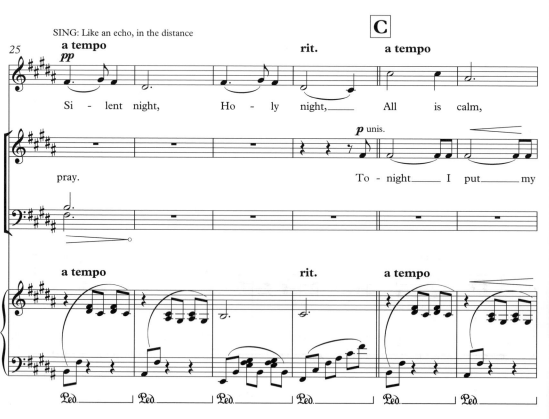

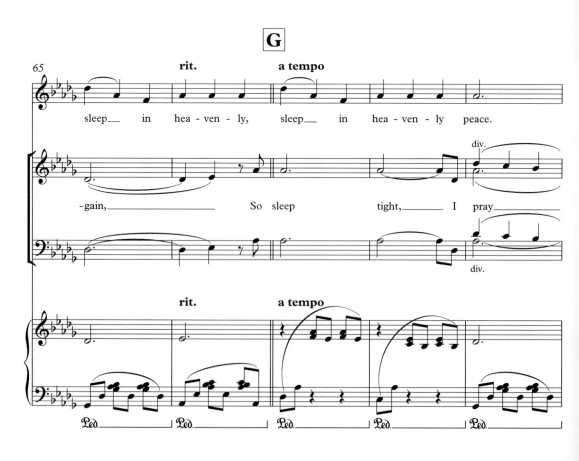

Solo: O Come, All Ye Faithful

The Infant King

(SATB and Children's Choir)

Basque Noël
arr. Christopher Robinson

39

mf

-by!___ Hush, do not wake___ the in - fant King. Soon will come sor - row

mf

46

with___ the morn - ing, Soon will come bit - ter grief___ and weep - ing:

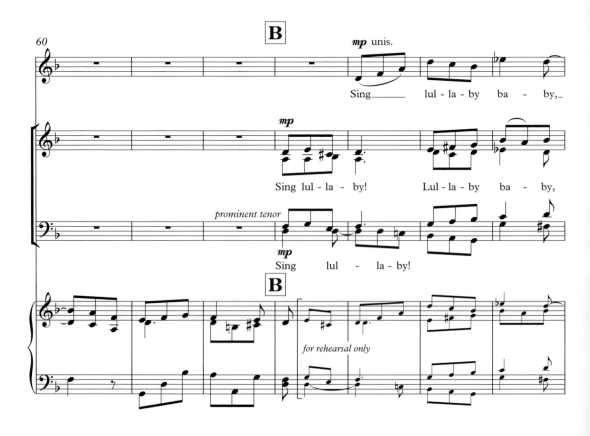

for rehearsal only

now a - doz - ing, sing lul - la - by! Hush, do not

now__ a - doz - ing, sing lul - la - by! Do not wake__ the in - fant

sing lul - la - by! Do not wake the in - fant

King.__ Soon__ comes the cross, the nails,__ the pierc - ing, Then in the grave__ at

King. Soon the cross,

break - ing: Sing lul - la - by! mm

break - ing: Sing lul - la - by!

Sing lul - la - by!

for rehearsal only

Sing lul - la - by!

The Infant King

(Children's Choir version)

Basque Noël
arr. Christopher Robinson

-by! Hush, do not wake the in - fant King. Soon will come sor - row

with___ the morn - ing, Soon will come bit - ter grief___ and weep - ing:

Sing___ lul - la - by! Sing lul - la - by! Sing lul - la - by!

* Optional second part from bar 71-83.

ing of Eas - ter, glad - some morn - ing, Con-quer-ing death, its bond - age

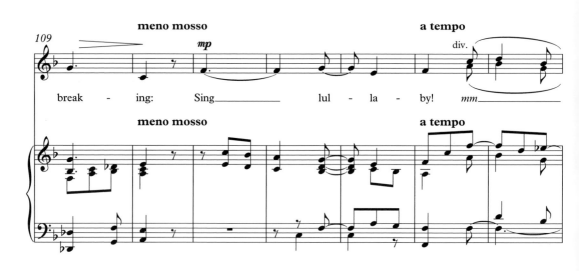

break - ing: Sing_____ lul - la - by! _mm_____

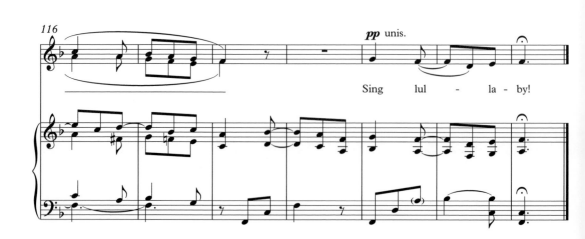

Sing lul - la - by!

Rudolph, the red-nosed reindeer

Words and music: Johnny Marks
arr. Richard Allain
(additional lyrics by Richard Allain)

44

* If performed by children's choir alone, sing cued notes.

52

Silent night

Joseph Mohr (1792-1849)
trans. John F. Young (1820-85)

Franz Xaver Gruber (1787-1873)
arr. James Whitbourn

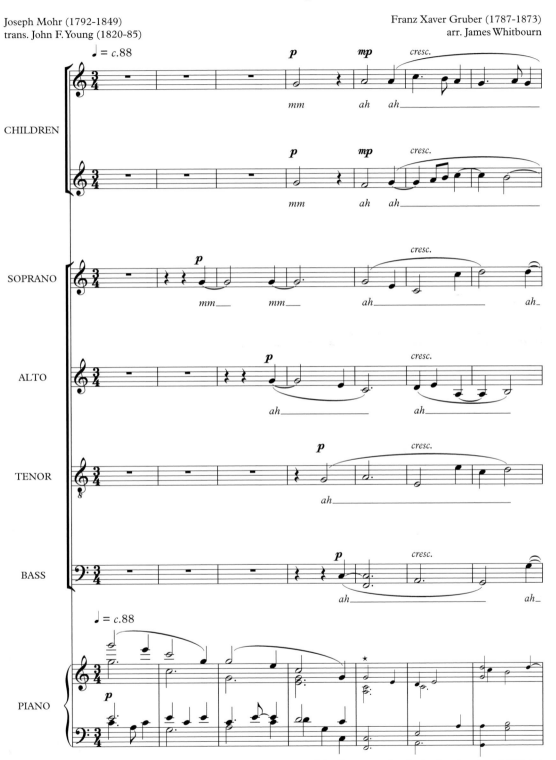

* Small notes are played only when there is no SATB choir

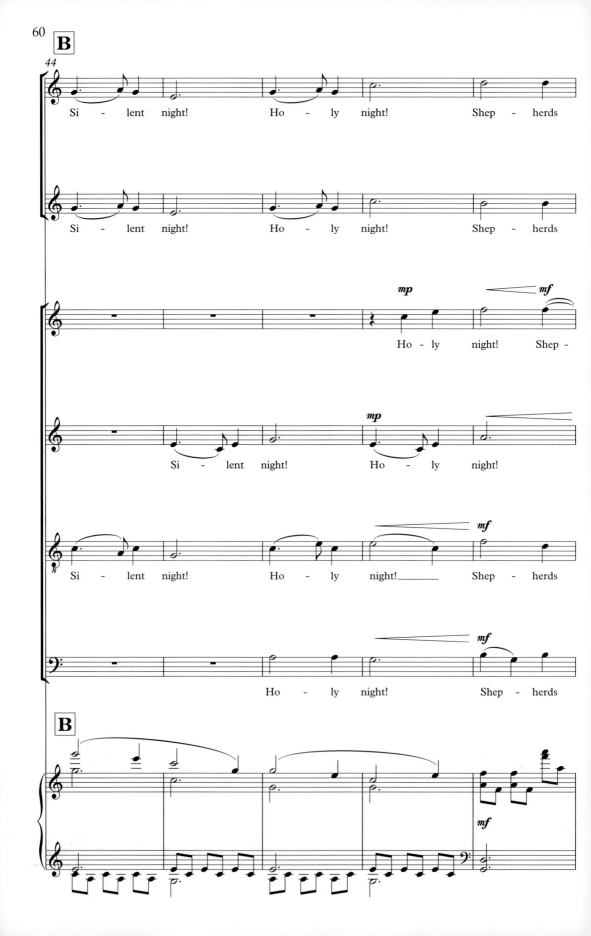

** Play only upper notes of r.h. when small notes are used

to my dear mother and nan

We three kings of Orient are

Words & music: John Henry Hopkins, Jr.
arr. Kenneth Hesketh

* This carol may be performed without SATB chorus by children's voices
and piano alone, or without children's voices with SATB and piano alone.

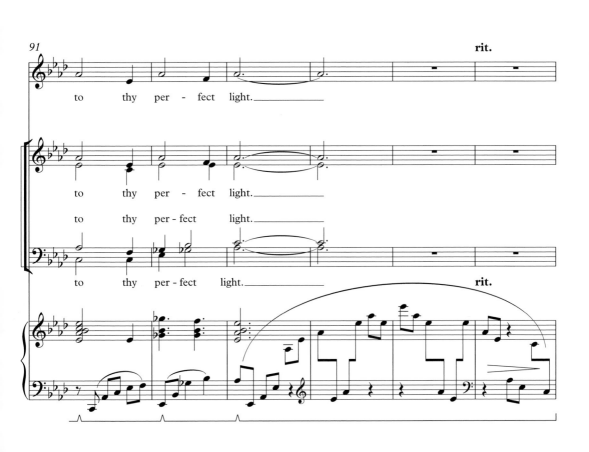

* When sung SATB alone, from bars 115-116 the sopranos should sing
the children's part. The sopranos should not sing the melody from bar 117-124.

* Play if performed without SATB chorus.

West - ward lead - ing, still pro - ceed - ing, Guide us to thy

West - ward lead - ing, still pro - ceed - ing, Guide us to thy

per - fect light, Guide us to thy per - fect light,

per - fect light, Guide us to thy per - fect light,